THE MATT MERTON
MYSTERIES

DEADLY NIGHT

Paul Blum

RISING★STARS

nasen

Helping Everyone Achieve

■ ■ ■ nasen

NASEN House, 4/5 Amber Business Village, Amber Close,
Amington, Tamworth, Staffordshire B77 4RP

Rising Stars UK Ltd.
22 Grafton Street, London W1S 4EX
www.risingstars-uk.com

Text © Rising Stars UK Ltd.
The right of Paul Blum to be identified as the author of this work has
been asserted by him in accordance with the Copyright, Design and
Patents Act, 1988.

Published 2010

Cover design: pentacorbig
Illustrator: Chris King, Illustration Ltd
Photos: Alamy
Text design and typesetting: pentacorbig/Clive Sutherland
Publisher: Gill Budgell
Editorial consultants: Lorraine Petersen and Dee Reid

British Library Cataloguing in Publication Data.
A CIP record for this book is available from the British Library.

ISBN: 978-1-84680-799-2

Printed by Craft Print International Limited, Singapore

THE MATT MERTON
MYSTERIES

CONTENTS

THE CRASH

The Crash happened in 2021. Alien spaceships crash-landed on Earth. Now the aliens rule the world. They have changed shape so they look like people. People call the aliens The Enemy. Since The Crash, people are afraid. They don't know who is an Enemy and who is a friend.

An organisation called The Firm keeps order on the streets. The Firm keeps people safe from Enemy attacks — or do they?

People are going missing and the Earth is becoming colder and darker all the time. A new ice age is coming ...

ABOUT MATT MERTON

Matt Merton works for The Firm. He often works with **Dexter**. Their job is to find and kill The Enemy. They use Truth Sticks to do this.

But Matt has problems. He has lost some of his memory and cannot answer some big questions.

Where has **Jane**, his girlfriend, gone?

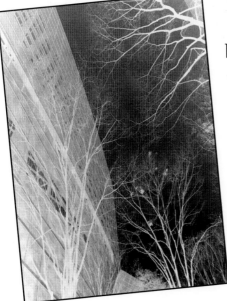

How did he get his job with **The Firm**?

Matt thinks The Firm is on the side of good. But he is not sure …

CHAPTER 1

Matt Merton went into the cafe. It was late.

'You're out late tonight, Matt. Working again?' asked Sam.

'No, I just can't sleep,' said Matt. 'I need a coffee. Extra hot with an extra shot, please.'

'Coffee won't help you sleep,' Sam said. He made the drink anyway.

Matt looked around him. He was the only customer. 'How much longer can you keep this cafe open?' he asked Sam. 'You can't be making much money.'

'I've already stayed open too long,' said Sam. 'I should have closed down months ago but I like the routine of coming to work. Talking to customers makes life feel more like it used to be.'

Matt smiled. 'Remember what it was like before The Crash?' he said.

Sam nodded. 'I was rushed off my feet. The local school and students from the university kept me busy.'

Matt felt himself shiver. 'Then the university was destroyed by a bomb ...' he said quietly.

'What happened to the school?' Sam asked.

'I don't think there are enough children to go to it now,' said Matt. 'A lot of them disappeared on the night of The Crash.'

Matt bit his lip. He shouldn't have spoken of that night. Sam's wife and child had disappeared on the night that the aliens crash-landed on Earth.

Sam didn't say anything but Matt saw a tear in his eye as he handed Matt his drink.

'Thanks, Sam,' said Matt. He drank the coffee quickly and left the cafe.

Matt walked for a long time. He didn't know where he was going. It was snowing and the streets were empty.

Since The Crash, the cold was getting worse every day. A new ice age was coming, Matt was sure of it. How would the people of the city survive the snow and ice? Many would starve or die of cold. The snow just didn't stop falling.

Matt was cold, but he was thinking about the school. He wanted to find out what had happened to it. He walked up to the old building. Then he saw there was a light on inside.

'That's not right,' Matt thought. The school had clearly been shut down. Why would anybody want to go into an empty building?

Matt thought of Sam. This had been his son's school. Maybe Matt could find something out about what had happened to him. Every lead was worth following. Matt had a strong feeling that he should go inside, even if it was dangerous.

He tried the door but it was locked. Matt found a small window and broke the glass. He went inside.

Matt went up the stairs. The building was dirty and full of broken furniture. The floor was covered with smashed glass and torn books. Matt couldn't remember the last time he had read a book. There was no time to relax when you worked for The Firm.

The school was silent. Since The Crash there were only a few children on the streets. The Firm did not trust children so most of them stayed hidden indoors. The Firm said children worked with The Enemy and had 'the look'. Matt was told to question any children he saw so he followed his orders.

Why are children so dangerous? Matt asked himself. But he could not remember the answer. He had worked for The Firm for so long he couldn't really remember life before them and The Crash.

CHAPTER 2

Matt reached the room where the light was on. He could not believe his eyes.

There was no broken furniture or smashed glass in here. Instead, this room held a large computer screen and a small boy.

Matt looked at the computer screen. He saw his photograph on it. The boy was reading Matt's file from The Firm. He saw pictures of Dexter and Jane too. The boy didn't move, so Matt stood next to him and started to read. He scanned Jane's file and saw the words 'Route 6', 'Enemy' and 'on the run'. Maybe Jane was still alive after all, but what was the boy doing?

'What are you doing here?' asked Matt. 'What is your name?'

The boy said nothing.

Matt took out his Truth Stick. Was the boy an Enemy? Why was he looking at those files? Only The Firm's computers would have pictures like that: the boy must be a hacker. But why was he using a computer in an empty school?

Matt felt angry. What was really going on here? Who was this boy working for? He must know where Jane was. Matt was going to get the truth out of him.

'What's your name?' he asked again. The boy still said nothing.

'What's your mother's name?' Matt shouted.

The boy began to cry.

'I need answers,' said Matt. 'What are you doing here in the middle of the night? Why are you hacking into The Firm? Where is Jane?'

The boy just kept on sobbing. The noise was getting on Matt's nerves but it was also making him feel sad. Matt knew he had to use the Truth Stick. The boy had 'the look', but he was just a kid after all. What should he do?

CHAPTER 3

Matt knew he had to get some help. He also needed time to calm down. He didn't want to do something he would regret. Matt locked the door so the boy could not get away, then he called his partner, Dexter.

'Merton, this had better be good,' said Dexter when he picked up his phone. 'It's the middle of the night.'

'I think I've found an Enemy in the school,' said Matt. 'He's hacking into The Firm's computer.'

'What are you doing in a school anyway?' asked Dexter.

'I saw a light. I broke in,' said Matt.

'That makes perfect sense. I always break into places that leave their lights on at night,' said Dexter.

'He may be an Enemy, Dexter, but he's just a kid. He's looking at pictures of both of us. He's got our files from The Firm.'

Matt didn't say anything about seeing Jane's file. He wasn't sure why, but he didn't want Dexter to know that he was still thinking about Jane.

There was a long silence at the end of the line.

'Wait there,' said Dexter. 'I'm on my way.'

Deadly Night

Matt left the building and waited in the street.

It was still snowing. It was colder than ever.

Then Matt heard a noise in the sky. It was a low thumping sound that grew louder and louder. He looked up and saw a helicopter. It stopped above the school.'

'What's going on?' thought Matt. 'That can't be Dexter. He would like to fly in and be a hero, but he's not that fast.'

Suddenly the sky lit up and there was a loud bang.
Matt was knocked over by the blast. He found
himself choking on smoke.

'What are they doing?' he coughed. 'Dexter was
going to meet me here.'

The helicopter circled the school to make sure it was
completely destroyed.

Then the helicopter flew away.

CHAPTER 4

Matt's phone rang. It was Dexter. 'Dexter what have you done?' yelled Matt.

'Just taking care of business,' Dexter replied.

'But you've killed the boy and destroyed whatever he was working on.'

'What you said on the phone sounded dangerous,' said Dexter. 'We can't risk The Enemy hacking into The Firm.'

'But we didn't know that for sure,' Matt replied. 'It was just a guess.'

'Sometimes you have to act first and ask questions later,' said Dexter. 'Your trouble, Matt, is that you think too much.'

'Aren't we paid to think?' asked Matt, angrily.

Dexter just laughed. 'Look Merton, you got out of the building,' said Dexter. 'Why are you making such a fuss? We couldn't take any chances.'

'Yes, I did get out but the boy didn't. He must be dead. Now we'll never find out who he was working for,' shouted Matt.

'Matt. You got out,' said Dexter.

'Yes, but the boy must be dead! We could have taken him in. Why?' shouted Matt.

'I'm just doing my job, Merton,' said Dexter in a cold voice. 'I think you should get on and do yours. Stop sticking your nose into things that don't concern you.'

Matt was very angry. His legs were shaking as he walked away.

A boy was dead. The school was still on fire. Jane was still missing.

And Matt knew he wouldn't sleep tonight.

QUIZ

1. What drink does Matt order?

2. Is Sam's cafe doing well?

3. What happened to Sam's family on the night of The Crash?

4. Which building did Matt visit?

5. How did he get inside the building?

6. What was the boy looking at?

7. What questions did Matt ask the boy?

8. Where was the boy hacking into?

9. What did the helicopter do?

10. Why was Matt so angry with Dexter?

GLOSSARY

hacker – someone who uses a computer to access private information

regret – feeling sorry for something you shouldn't have done

routine – doing the same things regularly

take any chances – take the risk

ANSWERS

1. Coffee (extra hot with an extra shot)

2. No, it has hardly any customers

3. They disappeared

4. The school building

5. He broke a window

6. Pictures and files of Jane, Matt and Dexter on a computer

7. His name and his mother's name

8. The Firm

9. The helicopter bombed the school and killed the boy

10. He wanted to question the boy about who he worked for and about Jane

CASE FILE

AUTHOR NAME
Paul Blum

JOB
Teacher

LAST KNOWN LOCATION
London, England

NOTES

Before The Crash taught in London schools. Author of *The Extraordinary Files* and *Shadows*. Believed to be in hiding from The Firm. Wanted for questioning. Seems to know more about the new ice age than he should ...

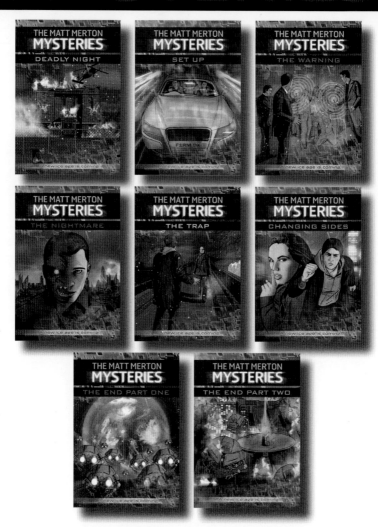